THE WEATHERMAN

Contents

Adapted by Benjamin Hulme-Cross

THE WEATHERMAN

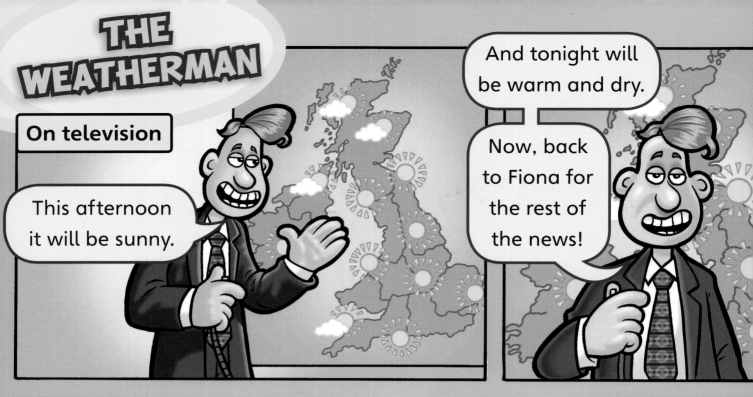

On television

This afternoon it will be sunny.

And tonight will be warm and dry.

Now, back to Fiona for the rest of the news!

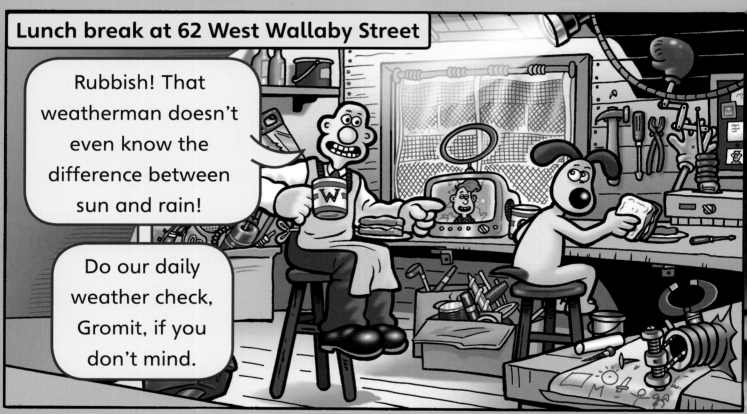

Lunch break at 62 West Wallaby Street

Rubbish! That weatherman doesn't even know the difference between sun and rain!

Do our daily weather check, Gromit, if you don't mind.

Sunny, he says! Sunny!

That weatherman is always wrong!

One day, he said it would rain and I got sunburned! The next day, he said it would be sunny and I nearly froze my ears off!

Let's send a letter to the TV station. Write this down, please, lad.

If he forecasts rain, we get sunburned! If he forecasts sunshine, we get thunderstorms!

Dear TV Station Manager, Every day, your weatherman is wrong!

I will build a machine to help with the weather forecasts.

And Ron Winterbottom, your weatherman, needs a new job!

The local TV station, a few days later

This letter is from Wallace, a local inventor. Ha ha ha! It's funny, isn't it, Ron?

No!

Oh come on, Ron, it's just a bit of fun. I might ask Fiona to read it out on the news.

But that will make me look like an idiot!

Well, maybe you should get your weather forecasts right more often.

May I see that letter?

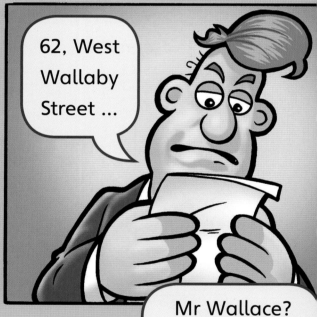

62, West Wallaby Street ...

Mr Wallace? It's Ron Winterbottom from the TV. Are you home?

A few minutes later

Nearly home, Gromit. We'll have a nice cup of tea and a ...

Oh no!

Quick, Gromit! Something's gone terribly wrong!

We have to get inside and ...
Oh dear! I don't like the look of that thundercloud! It's right outside our front door!

Yikes! Get the front door open, Gromit!

5

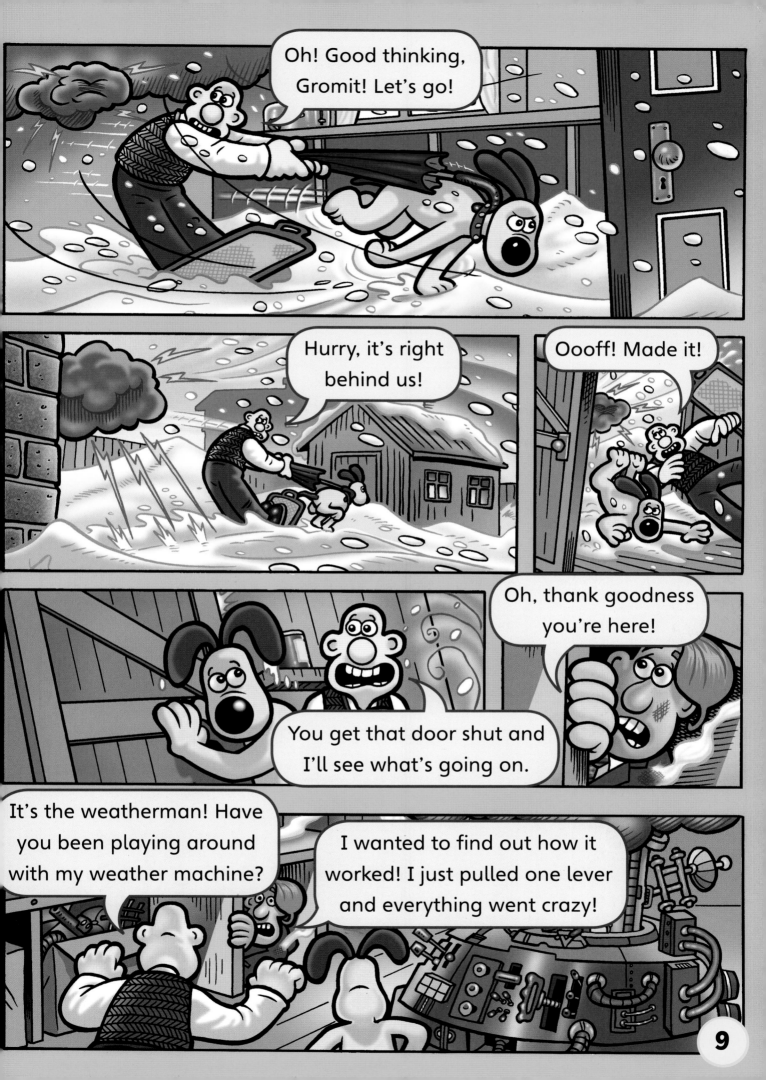

9

10

62 West Wallaby Street, Christmas Eve. Wallace is checking everything is done before bed.

Presents wrapped and under the tree ...

... done.

Turkey stuffed and in the oven ...

... done.

Shaun in kennel asleep ...

... yes.

Shaun's present is one frozen vegetable snowman ...

... done.

Christmas present wrapping machine, switched off ...

... done.

Well, Gromit. I think that's everything.

Sleep tight.

Outside, Shaun decides that he doesn't want to stay in his kennel on Christmas Eve. He'd rather be in the house ...

Since he can't find any food, he decides to explore upstairs ...

He spots the Christmas present wrapping machine. That looks like fun!

He manages to switch it on ... but he gets more than he bargained for!

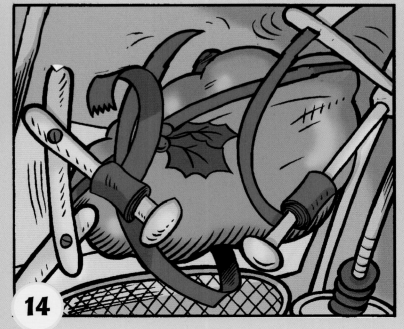

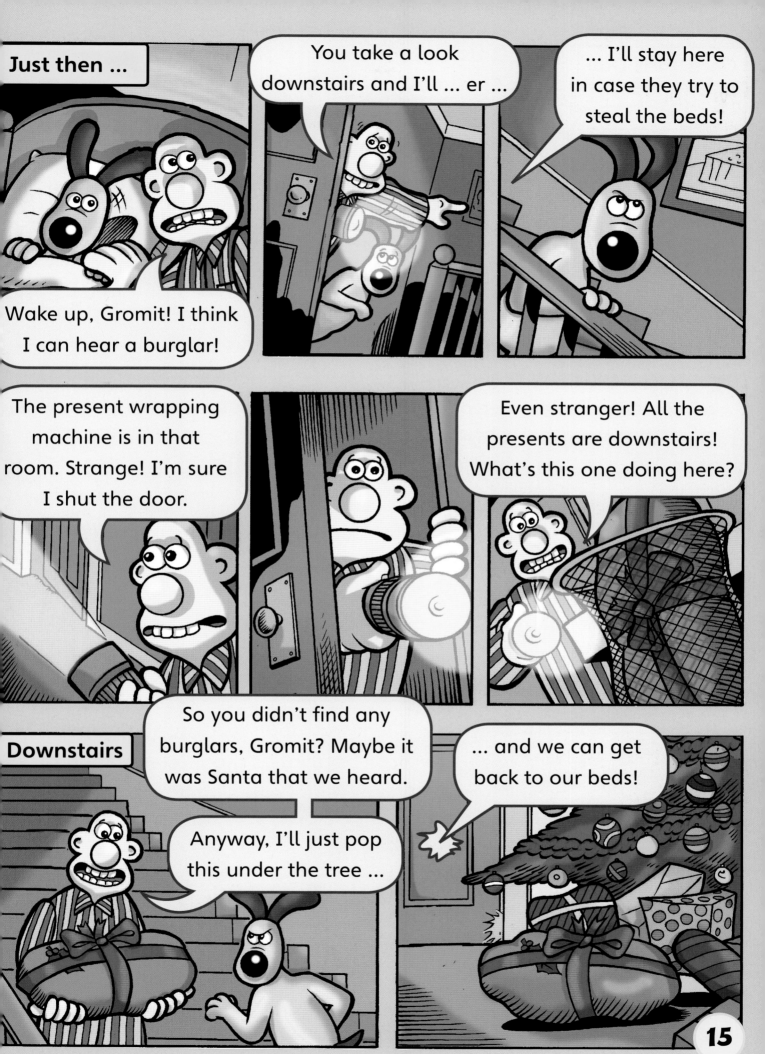

15